ripple
WORKBOOK

Ripple Workbook
Published by Lasting Impact Press
405 Mason Ct., Suite 113
Fort Collins, CO 80524

Copyright © 2015 Chris Hutchinson

Lasting Impact Press and its logo are trademarks of Lasting Impact Press.
Cover and interior design by Launie Parry, Red Letter Creative
Interior illustrations by Chris Hutchinson

Library of Congress Cataloging-in-Publication Data

Hutchinson, Chris
Ripple Workbook: Exercises for leadership that works
by Chris Hutchinson.

ISBN: 978-1-942492-03-0

1. Business / leadership 2. Organizations / Organizational effectiveness
3. Success in business / mentoring & coaching

Printed in the United States of America
2015 - First Edition

Special Sales

For special quantity discounts for your corporation, organization, or special-interest group, please contact Lasting Impact Press at www.lastingimpactpress.com.

ripple
WORKBOOK

EXERCISES FOR LEADERSHIP THAT WORKS

CHRIS HUTCHINSON

lasting impact

PRESS

Introduction

This workbook is to help you get into action with the principles and practices in *Ripple: A Field Manual for Leadership that Works*. As this workbook is designed as to accompany *Ripple*, if you don't already have a copy please go to rippleleader.com to get one.

Here's the overall process of using this workbook to further develop your leadership:

Congratulations for going beyond just reading and getting into real action. As a leader, the example you live out is more powerful than anything you think or say. Using this workbook to organize your actions will help you hurdle the knowing-doing gap so many other people get stalled by. Your team and your organization are lucky to have you as their leader.

Good luck! And let me know how you're doing and what results you get at chris@trebuchetgroup.com.

1. **Do a Self-Assessment**
   Step through the assessments of all the practices to determine your most significant gap, or area of improvement. Armed with this information, you're ready to...

2. **Build your own Action Plan**
   This section helps you create a plan to improve those areas where small changes can result in significant, positive impact. You'll step through...
   - **Desired outcome(s)** of your improvement project
   - **Major steps / milestones** along the way
   - **Support needed** to be successful as quickly and effectively as possible
   - **Principle(s) at play** to make sure you're focused on what's most important
   - **Practices(s) to use** to get better, including specific exercises to increase your understanding and effectiveness
   - **Learning from exercises** to pull your thinking and actions together
   - **Final results**, measured against your outcome
   - **Next steps** on your journey of continuing improvement

3. **Implement your Action Plan**
   As your plan contacts reality, you may need to tweak and adjust it. Be flexible as you focus on achieving as many of the desired outcomes as you can. Be sure to document your learnings as you go.

4. **Do a Self-Reassessment**
   Reinforce your action-based learning by looping back to the self-assessment, using a different color pen or markings to see where you want to make changes next.

5. **Lather. Rinse. Repeat.**
   Remember that Ripple Leadership is a process. While working on your leadership will result in specific improvements, the real impact is in the ripples that spread out from the actions you take on an ongoing basis. And the more you work on your leadership, the farther you can skip your stones.

How this workbook is laid out

To support your action-based learning, this workbook is laid out in the following manner

- **The Six Principles of *Ripple* Leadership**
  A short reminder of the overall principles

- **Practices Self-Assessment**
  These structured self-questions from *Ripple* to enable you to honestly assess where you are on each practice and determine where you'd like to improve.

- **Action Planning**
  Action plans are laid out for you to capture your current needs and challenges, to note results of specific exercises, and to chart your improvement.

- **Leadership Development Exercises**
  These exercises are reproduced from *Ripple* with some slight tweaks to enable you to have room for your thoughts, explorations, and findings.

- **Personal Insights**
  This section is for capture your thinking about yourself, other important people, and your organization, and includes summaries of the important points from the appropriate sections from *Ripple* for reference.

  - *Leading Yourself* - 10 pages

  - *Leading Others* - 10 pages
    Coworkers / Employees - 5 at 2 pages each
    Clients / Customers - 5 at 2 pages each

  - *Leading the Organization* - 10 pages

If you mark up your copy to the point where you want some clean space, feel free to visit rippleleader.com, download the complimentary electronic version, and print whichever pages you need. Don't let any barriers, however small, get in the way of your own leadership excellence!

The Six Principles of Ripple Leadership

These principles are operating at all times on you as a leader and on the people and organization you lead. The good news is that, along with *Ripple*, this workbook will help you leverage these principles for your benefit and the benefit of everyone who is connected with your organization.

Principle 1 –
Leaders' effectiveness is proportional to how well they know themselves.
As a state of being, deep self-alignment is the foundation for a leader's potential impact.

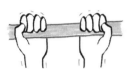

Principle 2 –
Leaders are judged more by what they don't than by what they do.
As leader, no one will force you to do the things that matter – and neither will they forget if you don't.

Principle 3 –
People discover their best selves through being respected by a leader.
Leaders who listen, look for, and uncover others' strengths create capacity and commitment.

Principle 4 –
People multiply a leader's power only as much as that power is shared.
The success of a leader is determined by how much he or she can positively enable others.

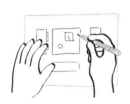

Principle 5 –
Organizations are designed to get the results they are getting.
Want different results? Design a different organization.

Principle 6 –
Organizations generating waste are generating opportunities for improvement.
Lead the organization to minimize waste and optimize output.

Ready? Let's get started creating some ripples

Ripple Practices Self Assessment

The questions below are to help you explore further which practice is most beneficial to start working on.

Look at each set of statements and mark where you are on the continuum of that practice. You may want to use a different color or symbol and write down the date in the margin each time you assess yourself to track your progress.

Don't cheat yourself. Dishonest assessments are not valuable to you, your team, or your organization.

How well do you know yourself, your aspirations, and your strengths?

Personal self-understanding is vital to building a strong foundation for your leadership.

Where are you right now on the following practices?

Practice 1.1 | **Decide what matters most**

| I have not yet defined my values. | I understand and use my values every day. | Others need to follow my values. |

Practice 1.2 | **Chart your own course**

| I work day-to-day and hope for the best. | My picture of the future pulls me forward toward it every day. | I live on the horizon, sometimes forgetting about today. |

Practice 1.3 | **Know where you're awesome**

| My capabilities are simply whatever I do. | I have validated and apply my strengths, avoiding my weaknesses. | I'm clear that other people need to work around my capabilities. |

How are you in action around your personal responsibilities as a leader?

The action orientation of a leader can make the difference between making things happen and allowing circumstances to rule.

Where are you right now on the following practices?

Practice 2.1 | **Do the hard stuff**

| I do what's in front of me in the moment | I focus on and always do what's most important | I have no patience for anything but what's most important to me |

Practice 2.2 | **Risk and be resilient**

| I do what's easy and practical | I constantly challenge myself to do better | I get bored if I'm not taking bet-the-farm risks |

Practice 2.3 | **Charge your own batteries**

| My body better keep up with my schedule | I take care of my body, mind, and spirit | I spend most of my time improving myself |

How are you honestly and deeply respecting each other person?

The amount of respect a leader provides determines how available others' strengths are for everyone to use.

Where are you right now on the following practices?

Practice 3.1 | Trust or have nothing

| I withhold trust until the other person earns it | I begin my relationships trusting the other person | I find others take advantage of my trust |

Practice 3.2 | Mission first. People second. You? Last.

| I take care of my needs first | I take care of others' needs first, then mine | I only take care of others' needs |

Practice 3.3 | Assume most of your stories are wrong

| My stories are always right, so why ask? | I set aside my stories to find out what is real | I ignore warning signs and instead hope for the best |

Practice 3.4 | Look for diamonds in the dirt

| I wait for people to impress me | I see people's potential for greatness | I believe in people much more than they do |

Practice 3.5 | Help them figure out how to fish

| I provide the right answers to help people | I ask questions that explore others' thinking | I'm told people feel their ideas are never good enough |

How are you positively enabling each person to succeed?

Your willingness and ability to remove barriers for others – and sometimes even yourself – determines how much their strengths can be harnessed for everyone's benefit.

Where are you right now on the following practices?

Practice 4.1 | **Meet them at eye level**

I expect people to meet me where I am	I meet each person where he or she is	I start with everyone like they don't know anything

Practice 4.2 | **Lead from a half-step ahead**

The people I lead don't influence my pace	I strive to stay just slightly ahead of everyone	I maintain distance between myself and my people

Practice 4.3 | **Light their torches**

I set equally high expectations for everyone I work with	I work to tap the strengths and passions of everyone	People decide how they want to show up

Practice 4.4 | **Be their outfitter and guide**

Sink or swim— it's up to them	I provide resources and encourage with real feedback	I can smother people with "help"

How are you structuring the organization and people for success?

The extent to which you understand the design of the organization, as well as effective ways of fitting the moving parts together, determines your success and the success of the entire enterprise.

Where are you right now on the following practices?

Practice 5.1 | **Use everyone's crayon in the picture**

I decide the vision of where we need to go	I build ownership in a shared picture of the future	Whatever people envision is the direction we should go

Practice 5.2 | **Know what's in the black box**

I focus on what I can control - my job is to do my job	I work to understand how our organizational components interact	I know how the organization works better than anyone

Practice 5.3 | **Work backward from the outcome**

I dive in and start improving things from where we are	I work toward our shared picture of success	I won't allow changes unless we know the end result

Practice 5.4 | **Make the right things easy**

Working hard to do the right thing is just what you have to do	I change the organization to make the right things easy	I encourage people to do whatever works for them

How are you influencing the organization to get better and better?

The extent to which you can influence how well organizational systems are run will determine how consistent and efficient everyone can be working together.

Where are you right now on the following practices?

Practice 6.1 | **Do or do not...there is no exception**

| I allow exceptions if there are special circumstances | I allow exceptions as long as they are made permanent | I enforce the process and rules no matter what |

Practice 6.2 | **Put a speedometer on everyone's dashboard**

| My job is to tell people when they are off target | I make sure people have the information to self-regulate | The numbers dictate what we need to do |

Practice 6.3 | **Enable eggshell structure**

| The structure makes decisions for everyone, including me | I make sure our structure encourages the best in people | I make sure our structure doesn't get in the way of anyone |

Practice 6.4 | **Go beyond the status quo**

| If it isn't broken, I don't fix it | I'm constantly tweaking what and how we do things | I break things so we have to fix them |

Often the best practice to work on is not the one where there is the most significant difference between where you are and where you want to be. Instead, it is the one that is holding you and your team back from success, showing up again and again as a stumbling block people trip over.

Asking yourself what's holding you back will begin to uncover paths to success that you haven't yet looked at.

Writing in this workbook is a highly effective way to begin moving from thought into action.

Which practices stand out as important and urgent for you to address?

How will working on them help you, others, and the organization?

What order do you believe they need to be addressed / improved?

What's holding you back from working on them?

Action Planning

Desired outcome(s)

What do you want or need as the outcome of this improvement project?

For yourself?

For your team?

For your organization?

Major steps / milestones

What are the significant steps to complete this project? What milestones would you pass along the way?

Support needed

What help could enable you to be successful as quickly and effectively as possible?
This could be systems, people, or both.

Principle(s) at play

What Ripple *principles are involved in or could influence the results you want to achieve?*

Practices(s) to use

Which Ripple *practices are most likely needed to get better results? Note which exercises you think will help you increase your understanding and effectiveness.*

Learning from exercises

This spot is to capture your learnings as you implement your action plan. What have you learned, either positively or negatively around your thinking or doing, from the exercises?

Final Results

What did you end up with? How do your results compare to your desired outcomes?

Next steps

What will you do next on your journey of continuing improvement?

Action Planning

Desired outcome(s)

What do you want or need as the outcome of this improvement project?

For yourself?

For your team?

For your organization?

Major steps / milestones

What are the significant steps to complete this project? What milestones would you pass along the way?

Support needed

What help could enable you to be successful as quickly and effectively as possible?
This could be systems, people, or both.

Principle(s) at play

What Ripple *principles are involved in or could influence the results you want to achieve?*

Practices(s) to use

Which Ripple *practices are most likely needed to get better results? Note which exercises you think will help you increase your understanding and effectiveness.*

Learning from exercises

This spot is to capture your learnings as you implement your action plan. What have you learned, either positively or negatively around your thinking or doing, from the exercises?

Final Results

What did you end up with? How do your results compare to your desired outcomes?

Next steps

What will you do next on your journey of continuing improvement?

Leadership Development Exercises

Slightly modified from *Ripple*, these exercises are reproduced here with more room for your thoughts and findings. The section that follows these exercises includes pages reserved for more refined thinking about yourself, the people you work with, and the organization you serve.

Exercise 1.1 | **Explore your own values**

This exercise is meant to help you begin to understand what you hold most dear and why you value what you value. There are so many versions of this exercise that I can't attribute the simple brilliance of it to any one person. Use the table of values below to complete the following activities. The blank areas are for you to write in values that you don't see on the table.

Abundance	Flexibility	Open-mindedness	Wisdom
Achievement	Fun	Patience	
Autonomy	Friendship	Power	
Beauty	Freedom	Productivity	
Challenge	Generosity	Prosperity	
Communication	Growth	Quality	
Competence	Happiness	Recognition	
Competition	Harmony	Respect	
Creativity	Health	Risk Taking	
Curiosity	Hope	Security	
Decisiveness	Humor	Service	
Dependability	Independence	Simplicity	
Discipline	Innovation	Spirituality	
Diversity	Integrity	Strength	
Effectiveness	Intelligence	Teamwork	
Efficiency	Joy	Transparency	
Empathy	Kindness	Trust	
Equality	Love	Truth	
Family	Loyalty	Variety	

1. **Determine your top 10 values.** First, cross out all values that don't make your top 10.

2. **Reduce the list to your top 3 values.** Next, underline those top 3.

3. **Reduce the top 3 to the top-most value for you.** (Yes, it's hard.) Box in your number one value.

4. **Dig down to get more insight into what's most important for you.** Once you've identified your values, think about how they show up in your work and home life, and write this down below. To take this further, spend another few minutes and write out what your top values mean in your own terms and using real-life examples or stories that demonstrate them.

Refer to this over time and refine as needed to give yourself the best chance of harnessing your values to get where you most want to end up.

Exercise 1.2a | **Picturing the Future you most want**

This simple method will enable you to begin extracting the elements of your own personal vision. The best part about this exercise, which I call Picturing the Future, is that it intentionally creates a very roughhewn vision. Instead of a wordsmithed-to-death, ready-to-chisel-in-granite proclamation, this is a roughed-out, simple set of criteria of what you want and don't want to help guide you on your journey.

1. **To start Picturing the Future, use the table below.**

2. **Imagine yourself five years in the future**. Everything is just how you want it. Ask yourself the following questions to clearly describe your desired future:

   - What have you achieved that you most wanted?

   - What have you avoided that you didn't want?

   - What have you preserved that you wanted to keep?

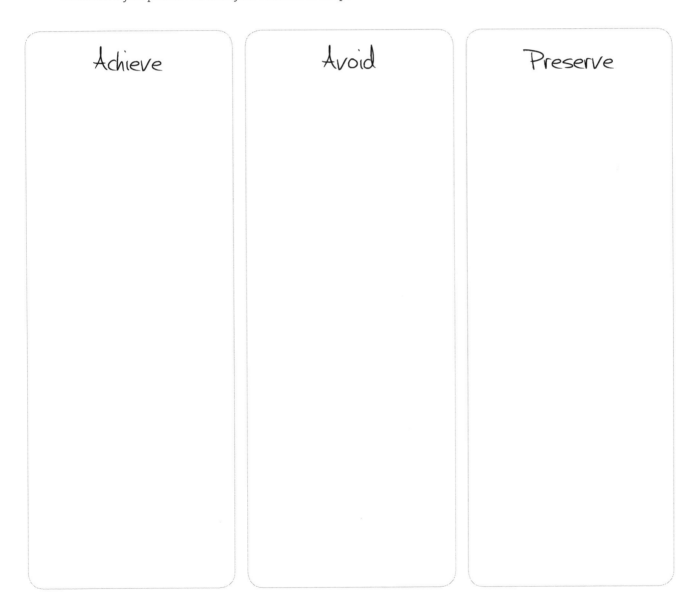

Achieve | Avoid | Preserve

3. **Write down at least five items for each category.** More is better. Notice that the questions are not a function of *HOW*. You want to get as close as possible to the end result of what you aspire to achieve. This approach grants you the most freedom and flexibility in the methods you might choose to pursue those goals.

4. **Review your list for must-haves and nice-to-haves.** Mark the must-haves.

5. **Use the list to guide your decision-making going forward.** When you need to make a significant decision, look at your list. Ask yourself how your available options help you achieve, avoid, and preserve what you have identified as most important to you. Choose the option that maximizes your success criteria and doesn't violate any of them, then proceed with confidence because that option is on the path to your desired future. If you don't have an option that works, see if you can change the conditions around the least-worst choice so that it fits with your success criteria. If you can't make it work, just say no. It's not on your path.

As you use tools like Picturing the Future, you will begin to more clearly discern your life's purpose: why you are here

Refine your achieve-avoid-preserve criteria as you use them to help yourself stay in alignment. If you have a choice that passes the filter yet you feel is still wrong, add the criteria that would screen it out. Likewise, if you have a choice that feels right yet doesn't pass, tweak your criteria set to enable it (and other opportunities like it) to be implemented. I encourage you to revisit this exercise at least annually to add further sharpness to your picture of your best personal future.

Exercise 1.2b | **Discern your purpose**

Lance Secretan has written 14 books on inspirational leadership and often speaks on helping people discern their purpose. He asks his readers Big Questions like, "Why are you here? What reality are you here to make happen?" While related to the Picturing the Future exercise you just did, this exercise goes further by looking at a larger, more universal picture and timeline out as far as you can imagine:

1. **Figure out what riles you up.** Take just a few minutes to write down whatever you see in the world that really ticks you off, personally and professionally. This is your time for a personal gripe session, so let loose! Those pet peeves are clues to the kind of reality you are here to help create. Pick your top-most irritants, and put a star next to each one.

2. **Pivot to the opposite.** Now take a few more minutes to imagine the opposite: You are in a distant future where all those starred conditions no longer exist because they are replaced with their complete opposites. (This is sometimes known as the "magic-wand" state, as if you had a magic wand and could wave it to get whatever you truly wanted.) While you've got those positive states in your mind, write down how you want things to be with as much detail as you can. Don't hold back! If you get stuck, look back to the previous exercise around your most important values. There should be some strong clues there about what you want for the universe.

3. **The difference between these two states is your purpose for being.** Without getting too metaphysical, let's say you're here to help the universe move from what's wrong with it to what's most needed. So take a few more minutes and write down what you see as the "delta," or difference, between what you don't want and what you do want.

While this is just the tip of the iceberg, this brief exercise is meant to provide you some clarification or validation of what you are working toward personally and professionally. Of course, now that you have more clarity, you also have a corresponding responsibility to make your positive future a reality. I believe this is what Gandhi meant when he said, "Be the change you want to see in the world." Making sure you are striving for a positive purpose will make your Ripple Leadership all the more powerful – and help your ripples reach far and wide.

Your purpose should bring out the very best in you: your deepest strengths, your greatest talents, your highest values.

After having a clear personal picture and connection to your personal passions, it's critical to understand your strengths to be able to use them to effectively lead yourself.

Exercise 1.3 | **Discover your sweet spot**

This exercise covers some activities you can use to uncover strengths you may not be fully aware of, and reaffirm those strengths you already know you have. Some of the components of this exercise could easily take longer than 15 minutes, and whatever time you invest here will pay significant dividends over the rest of your working career.

1. **Discover strengths that are hidden in plain sight**. Brainstorm a list of what you find easy and fun. Circle or add anything other people compliment you on. Look for patterns, then validate them with a trusted source, such as a significant other, to see if you've uncovered new strengths. Copy your strengths into the *Leading Yourself* section of this workbook.

2. **Take a third-party strengths assessment.** While it will likely take you longer than 15 minutes to take an assessment and interpret your results, it can be one of the best tools to help you objectively gauge your strengths. Ideally you should work with a person who can help you get as much out of the assessment as possible. We've never had a client regret spending time learning about their strengths. If you would like recommendations for assessments, contact Trebuchet Group for support.

3. **Journal your accomplishments each day for a week**. Take a few minutes each evening to write down in the *Leading Yourself* section or a journal about what you are most proud of and do really well. Also note what is frustrating and challenging to you. Stay alert for trends that can help you better identify your strengths. Electronic journals can be great. I enjoy the paper-based *10+ Journal* by Ian Matthews.

It's normal to be a little uncomfortable exploring your strengths. Many people feel they should know themselves well enough that this should be unnecessary. As I often tell my clients, "In the absence of other information, I believe I'm normal. So if you're just like me, you're normal. And if you're not like me, you're abnormal." Looking at your strengths from a slightly different perspective than usual can help you see what makes you unique, which in turn enables you to apply them in a deliberate way.

Exercise 2.1 | **What are you focusing on?**

Use this exercise to reflect on how importance and urgency are showing up in your life. Each part can be done separately. Each is designed to give you a chance to step back and evaluate how well you're focusing on those challenging and important activities for yourself as a leader.

1. **Shift a percentage of time you spend on urgent matters to more important things.** Take a few minutes and write down how you're spending your time below. Now get the opinions of at least two other trusted people to validate. If you're not happy with the results, choose one item this week that is important yet not urgent and commit to making that a priority. Once you start to see the important work you've done preventing fire drills, reinvest your recovered time in the next important and not urgent activity.

2. **Check the results you're seeking.** Take a few minutes and list your last three-to-five self-assigned projects. Note how much each builds capacity, relationships, and resilience of the organization, your people, and yourself. Note any patterns, positive or negative. Commit to shifting your focus on your next project to include at least one investment activity.

3. **Use activation energy to your advantage.** Pick one important activity that you can't seem to do. Brainstorm ways you could reduce the time and energy to get started to 30 to 120 seconds. Try out changes until you find what works for you.

Start small, and as your efforts bear positive results, reinvest the time and energy you saved for even better results. It's amazing what my company's clients have been able to achieve, even as they felt completely overloaded, through shifting their thinking and commitments around importance versus urgency.

Exercise 2.2 | **How to get past the snow drifts without bogging down**

This set of exercises is designed to increase your own awareness of what's getting in your way and how you can build momentum to get to the outcomes you desire.

1. **Examine what you're tolerating.** Write down what you're currently tolerating or working around in your organization or personal life. Don't hold back. When you're done, look for patterns or commonalities. Underline the tolerations that are most getting in your way or causing resource-intensive workarounds.

2. **Check out the part you're playing.** Next to your list of tolerations from step 1, write the "payoff" or benefit you derive from continuing to allow the significant tolerations. This requires a little mental gymnastics, as we tend not to think of getting something good from tolerating a situation or problem. Frequently clients find that by tolerating a problem, their payoff is that they put off or avoid some other issue they perceive as bigger or thornier.

3. **Brainstorm what you could do differently.** Look at one thing you're tolerating and the payoff that may be helping you tolerate it. What could you do differently to get the same payoff and at the same time reduce or eliminate the thing you're tolerating? It might require backing down the hill a ways to get to firm footing before you head up the hill again. Or potentially getting out of your comfort zone, at least a little.

Whatever's in your way, the best plan is to pick the smallest possible effort you can make with the highest chance of success, and then implement that change. The goal is to keep your momentum up and get past whatever's getting in your way in the simplest way you can.

To sustain momentum to carry you as far as possible, you'll need to make sure to keep your own energy and effectiveness up. No one else will do it for you.

Exercise 2.3 | **Keeping yourself sharp**

Paying attention to where you are spending energy and also giving yourself permission to invest time, energy, and resources into your own wellbeing are key to keeping yourself the best tool in your toolbox.

1. **Take stock of where you are right now.** Take a few minutes and write down how you are doing: Where are the same personal results taking more effort? Where is the same effort giving you worse results? What do these mean about your own personal sharpness mentally, emotionally, physically, and spiritually?

2. **Get out your whetstone.** Take a few minutes, show your significant other or trusted friend your results from step 1 above, and ask this person what you could do for yourself that you are not doing now. Pick one doable, promising thing from their suggestions or your own ideas, and get into action.

3. **Cultivate a habit of living your life in gratitude.** Spend one minute each night jotting down three things that you were grateful for that day in your journal or the *Leading Yourself* section. Recent research has shown this single action is more effective than psychoactive drugs in helping people deal with depression and unhappiness. Over time you will begin to feel less resistance to the changes you decide to make in your life.

Self-renewal is a habit that can make the difference between burning up your candle from both ends and being able to shine a light continuously to help other people see where to go.

Exercise 3.0 | **Dealing with your fishbowl**

To minimize the impact of distortion around your role, you'll need to become more aware of how it's affecting you and others. Then you can begin improving the clarity of communication and perception of others on the outside.

1. **Check for distortion outside the fishbowl.** Take a few minutes and make a list of the last several times you were misunderstood. If you can't recall any, find a trusted advisor – the kind of person who would tell you if you had spinach in your teeth – and ask him or her to share any times when what you said didn't make sense to someone. Look for any patterns to help you start seeing where and how your messages may be getting distorted.

2. **Check for scorch marks inside the fishbowl.** Take a few minutes and make another list in the of the last few times you reacted strongly to an update or news from others. Where might you be taking things too personally? Imagine positive intent and then see if and where the messages shift for you in meaning. Note any patterns that emerge.

3. **Pull out the glass polish.** With both lists in mind, take a few more minutes and project the patterns forward to your next probable encounter. Are there some challenges brewing? Is there something you are extra-sensitive about that is likely to come up? Jot down a quick script of how you want to do things differently to achieve different and better results. Then be proactive and initiate some better communication.

Copy your insights from this exercise to the **Leading Yourself** section of this workbook.

Keep practicing. You'll get credit from people even for attempts that don't end perfectly. When people understand your full intent, and they believe you see their intent as positive, your fishbowl will become so shiny and clear that hardly anyone will even notice it's there.

Exercise 3.1 | **To trust or not to trust, that is the question**

As a leader, you get what you project. So, to be respected, you must genuinely respect others. Don't trust blindly, but do show vulnerability and a willingness to admit that you could use some help. Until you do, you won't get that same openness from others. This exercise is focused on increasing your conscious awareness of the yin-yang of trust and control.

1. **Do a trust check.** Take a few minutes and write a list in of the people you work with and for, and rate yourself on a 0 to 10 scale on how trusting you are with each person. Be honest. Note any similarities or patterns in how you trust (or distrust).

2. **Do a control check**. Take a few minutes and reflect on the level of control versus trust you have in others. (You can use the list from the trust check.) Typically, the more a leader is controlling, the less he or she is trusting. Note these as well.

3. **Verify your results.** Take a few minutes and ask three people how much they think you trust them, also on a 0 to 10 scale. This would start out something like, "I'm noticing that sometimes I get so focused on results I might be coming across as not trusting or over-controlling. Would you be willing to help provide me some honest feedback? My goal is to build trust with you, not tear it down." After they rate you, you might ask for a specific example to help you understand. Thank them, then privately compare and contrast their numbers with the trust ratings you gave them.

4. **Start making deposits.** (OK, this is an investment, yet it's worth it.) Stephen Covey used the analogy of a bank-account, except this account holds the amount of trust you have from another person. Look for opportunities to make trust deposits whenever possible: apologize when you've made a mistake; help the other person avoid problems; ask for assistance when you need it; and admit your shortcomings. This would be a good time to create a page for each person in the **Leading Others** section in the back of this workbook. Note your attempts and successes in making deposits on each person's page. These actions all build trust and can make a positive difference in your relationship.

Challenging yourself to be more trusting sets the example and provides the environment for others to show you more trust as well. Without trust, there is really no relationship for you to rely on when you need to ask people to step up to help you and the organization.

Exercise 3.2 | **Align your needs with others and the business**

This practice can make discussions with anyone from unhelpful customer service personnel to upset significant others go more smoothly. Start small and build on your successes.

1. **Use a Cascading Needs Process for a minor conflict you're currently dealing with.** Take a few minutes and write down answers for each of the three steps of the process. Ask a trusted advisor for help if you get stuck trying to clarify the needs of the other person. Remember, the best answers are those that touch on unspoken yet demonstrated needs.

What are the overall needs of the situation / organization / shared future?

What are the other person's needs, especially those that are demonstrated yet unspoken?

What are your needs in this context that will enable you to advance all the needs above?

2. **Try it on for size.** Take five minutes (yes, it is that simple) and walk through the process with the person from start to finish. Script out the process if you want, and if the other person says, "Hey, are you trying something on me?", you can say, "Yes, I'm trying out a way to make sure what I'm doing is meeting your needs and the needs of the organization."

Lather. Rinse. Repeat. Look for other opportunities to try out this process. The more you align your needs with others', the more they will see you as a resource to get where they and the organization need to go.

RIPPLE WORKBOOK | Practice 3.2: **Mission first. People second. You? Last**

31

Exercise 3.3 | **Challenge your stories**

Our internal stories are our default settings – unless we actively challenge them. The trick is that the best time to challenge them is in the moment – right when the story is just about to cause an emotional reaction and physical action. These exercises are to equip you, through reflecting on previous interactions, to prepare you for interactions to come.

1. **Check your track record.** Reflect back on your experience with colleagues and friends. When have you been surprised that your initial impression about a person or situation was wrong? What did you unintentionally miss out on because of a wrong story? What will you do differently next time? Jot a few notes about your reflections below and copy any insights to the **Leading Yourself** section of this workbook.

2. **Change one of your stories.** Think about someone you get upset with easily. (If the story's really embedded, you will think of them as upsetting you!) Ask yourself what the *Crucial Confrontations'* authors call the Humanizing Question – "Why would a reasonable, rational, and decent person do that?" Start looking beyond what you experienced to shift the story you are telling yourself, the emotions you are feeling, and the actions you are taking. Write down your thinking in either the **Leading Yourself** section or their individual page and start working to interact differently with that person.

3. **Enlist an ally.** Find a person you trust and ask him to provide you with an alternate point of view for situations you're wrestling with. Ask him to challenge your stories and help you explore what could be happening for the other person. Be open and curious to his perspective, then see how that shifts your interactions with others.

Challenging your own stories is especially hard because they get so deeply embedded and "feel so real." The good news is that once you start shifting your perceptions, you begin to see that other people have qualities – often good qualities – you may have overlooked.

Exercise 3.4 | **Seek untapped greatness**

Where are you seeing dirt rather than diamonds? Since we tend to see what we're looking for, how much are you looking for diamonds in the first place? Here are some exercises to help you shift your thinking and get into a mining-for-strengths mindset.

1. **Do a greatness inventory.** Find a stretch of uninterrupted time. Write a list of the names of everyone you work with. Remember to include peers and any leaders you follow. Next to each, write down at least one thing that person is great at. For those people where all you can see is dirt, remember that weaknesses are often overdone strengths, and ask yourself what strength may be being overdone.

2. **Shift one thing by getting an outside-in perspective.** Take a few minutes each with three trusted people, and ask them how much they see you seeking success with other people versus avoiding failure. Look for common patterns, and change one of your behaviors to strengthen or shift in the direction of enabling success in others. Hint: choose the most doable change first to get energy to build on your successes.

3. **Boost one other person.** Briefly reflect on people you helped grow past their own limitations or the limitations of the positions they were in. Of the people you work with currently, who seems burdened by their limitations? If possible, use curiosity to explore the situation holding them back. "I've noticed this, and I'm wondering how it's working for you." Support as appropriate.

Since awareness tends to fade over time, it can be helpful to revisit your thinking around these exercises from time to time. On the **_Leading Others_** section pages for each person you work with, make sure to note where you see that person's diamond shine, what the dirt may be hiding, and progress as it's made. These are surefire ways to help you see the best in others and start enabling them to grow into their full potential.

Exercise 3.5 | **Move beyond just good questions**

Improving your questions to help others is just one component of deeply respecting others so they want to explore and learn more about what's possible for them. These exercises are meant to complement the material above and move you into action with your team members, peers, and leaders.

1. **Check your track record.** Take a few minutes and list the last five people who've left working with you. Why did they leave? How much did you help them grow past their own limitations or help move them toward their own destinations? Write down your findings and look for any patterns you want to build on or influence.

2. **Raise your awareness of your daily impact.** Take a few minutes and reflect on how much you are prescribing solutions through your questions. Hint: if you are asking people's opinion about an action – e.g. "Don't you think you should..." – it's often a solution in disguise. Another method is to pay attention to the questions you ask others for one day and jot them down in your *Leading Yourself* section for later reflection. Better yet, ask a trusted agent to observe the impact of your questions and then discuss the results with you privately. Again, look for patterns to strengthen or de-emphasize.

3. **Go make a difference.** Choose one person you want to help and spend fifteen minutes connecting with them around the challenges they are having with their work. Listen, listen, listen. Refrain from solving their problems. (Yes, it's hard!) At the end, ask how this helped or not, and offer to meet again if that would be helpful. Note your findings in your *Leading Yourself* section or on their page.

Good questions are a great start to open dialogue that empowers the other person to really engage. When you foster deep respect, you may be surprised at the richness that bubbles up in other people. Strong relationships are the best foundation for sharing and multiplying your influence for the benefit of your team, your organization, and ultimately, you.

Exercise 4.1 | **Meet others where they are**

Understanding where each person is starting from is a vital first step to helping that person grow. These exercises reveal where people are and help them develop in ways that help you, them, and the organization.

1. **Turn on your tractor beam.** Find out more about one of the people you work with. Invite her out for a 15-minute break. A way to start is asking what got her interested in her career field. Ask some or all of the questions listed in the *Ripple **Uncover Presenting Conditions*** sub-section. Be ready to answer any question you ask her. When you're done, write down the important points on her page in this workbook to help remember them. The following week, invest another 15 minutes in a different person.

2. **Seek dissatisfaction.** It's counterintuitive to actually look for dirt instead of diamonds. Yet people who are irritated, slightly on edge, or pushing back are often those who care the most about what needs to get done. Invite one of these people for a 15-minute break. Once there, set some healthy limits upfront to prevent a gripe session. Let her know that you wish you had more time yet you do have fifteen minutes. You noticed she seemed to want to do more than she was being allowed, and ask if she would be willing to give you a high-level overview of what she wants to make happen and what's holding her back. Listen, listen, listen. Write down the results of the conversation on her individual page in this workbook.

If you meet people where they are, you give them the best chance to succeed in their personal situations. And that will help people around you know that you're there to help them grow and contribute, no matter where they're starting from.

Exercise 4.2 | **Set the pace a half-step ahead**

Stepping out the right amount for your team and your organization to succeed can be a delicate balancing act. You need to pull the team forward, yet you need to be close enough to them to stay connected with them. These simple exercise steps can help you ensure you're at the right pace for your team and you to succeed together.

1. **Check your stride.** Ask three trusted people where they feel you are on the spectrum, from way behind, to alongside, to way ahead of the team. Make sure to tell them you are seeking a fully truthful answer. Note your findings here or in the *Leading Yourself* section. Adjust your stride as needed.

2. **Shift from pulling to encouraging.** Honestly answer the question: what would happen in the first day / week / month if you had to leave suddenly? Jot down your insights in the *Leading Yourself* section. Validate with a trusted source to find out how much you're pulling the team and organization. Shift the energy you were using to pull to helping others step forward. You'll know you're on the right track if your sudden departure would slow yet not stall the organization.

3. **Map out what being a half-step ahead would mean with different people.** For example:

Map out your own list of people you would most like to help. Ask yourself questions around what's next for them to uncover. Think how you might be able to lead them from just slightly ahead of where they are. Doing this on a regular basis, say, quarterly, will go a long way to helping people stretch themselves toward greater success.

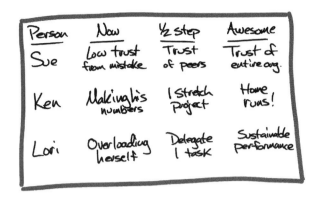

Person	Now	A Half-Step Ahead	Awesome

Note your thoughts on their individual pages in your workbook.

As you set out on a heading with your team close by, it is critically important to stay connected to what's happening with the team. Understanding their strengths and passions can help you make sure they are accessing the fuel and light that all of you need to go as far as possible together.

Exercise 4.3 | **Strike a spark**

These exercises will help both you and your employees plug into their hopes, values, and strengths. Using them regularly will not only help you help them, but the practices will also begin to take root in their own leadership skills so that they can help other people grow.

1. **Ask your top three people what would make their heart sing!** Explore with them where they would most like to go. This is more about the qualities of the future rather than actual work positions. A lower-pressure alternative is to ask people what their latest obsession is, i.e., what they focus on besides work. Then watch where they light up. Note your findings on their individual pages at the back of the workbook.

2. **Write down where you see the potential of each person on your team**. This could just be a short note on each person's page. Start looking for evidence where that is happening today and reinforce it. You will be surprised at how much untapped potential is available – and so will the people on your team.

3. **Write down the passions of your top three to five employees.** Stumped? Most leaders are – at first. Hint: what do they invest their time in, perhaps when they're not at work? It's amazing to me how often I get blank stares from leaders when I ask them what motivates each of their people, their peers, and their own leader. Take a few minutes and note on their pages what you see people get interested in and enthusiastic about.

4. **Give an earnest compliment to three different people each day.** Point out the specific behavior, why this behavior is important to your company's success, you, and them. You'll know you're really making a difference when you see people emulating this pay-it-forward behavior and doing the same. Keep track of your efforts and their responses in this workbook.

Knowing what we're best at, what matters, and where we ultimately want to go is critical preparation for the journey we need to take together. The next step is to help equip and outfit everyone for the journey.

Exercise 4.4 | **Guide and equip people for the journey**

People can and should do a lot of work on their own, and yet your involvement can make the difference between senseless struggle and hard-won satisfaction. These exercises are built to get you started finding out where you can make a difference helping to guide others and remove barriers from their path.

1. **Listen and empower**. Take a few minutes and connect with someone on your team. Ask, "What drives you crazy about your job?" Listen carefully and be curious, not defensive. Then ask, "How would you change it?" Take a few more minutes and brainstorm ways it could happen. Then sort the options by doability and impact, and support the person to try one. Keep track of progress on their pages in the workbook.

2. **Look where others are struggling.** Take a few minutes and write a list of your organization's projects in the *Leading the Organization* section. Reflect on where we're not making progress. Take some more time and ask where the challenges are. For example, how are we doing with direction, resources, and skills? Apply guidance, equipment, or organizational clout as needed to get the project unstuck.

3. **Check your ownership of other people's problems**. Take a few minutes and mentally catalog the unfinished work around you – paper, electronic, and projects. If you were suddenly able to do only half as much, what would you decide not to do? Start guiding and equipping others to reduce your level of involvement. Get assistance from a trusted agent if needed to start helping others help themselves more. Encourage yourself by writing results in the *Leading Yourself* section of your workbook.

4. **Write down what success would look like for each person on your team three to five years out.** Use each person's individual page at the back of the workbook. If you get stumped, be curious about how they got into what they do and look for the passion and interest. Project that interest forward. Where does it lead? Explore this with them. Bonus points depend on their level of engagement. You may have to overcome lack of momentum or stagnation.

You've just finished learning about and practicing better interpersonal leadership. The stones you just skipped will continue further into the organization, spreading positive ripples as they go. Next up are the policies, processes, and methods that need your help and the help of your people so your organization can run effectively and efficiently.

Exercise 5.1 | **Picture a shared future...together**

These exercise steps build on each other. Getting clarity for yourself and others about the future is a messy, imprecise process that will pay tremendous dividends to everyone involved even if the picture ends up a bit blurry. In other words, picturing a shared future is one of the best ways to involve people in creating an organization and goals they see as their own.

1. **Do some structured dreaming about what you want the organization to look like in the future.** Take a blank page in the ***Leading the Organization*** section of this workbook and 15 minutes to think about how you want the company to succeed. A good format is the Achieve-Avoid-Preserve method in the ***Chart your own course*** section (Exercise 1.2a). This step is critical to enable you to create a simple framework that you can feel confident allowing other people to build on.

Achieve	Avoid	Preserve

2. **Get other people's perspectives on what the future could look like**. Ask five different people to spend a few minutes with you on what they perceive success for the organization to look like three to five years into the future. Listen, listen, listen. When done, jot down their thoughts in the *Leading the Organization* section to compare their unique pictures of the future to yours and find the common connections.

3. **Allow others to sketch out their parts of the picture**. Put elements of your picture on the wall – the messier, the better to invite people to improve upon it – and leave it up for a few weeks. Hang a marker pen nearby with some sticky notes, and encourage people to make notes on it. If you've done a sufficient job getting the most important points covered, additions by others will augment and not hijack your vision of the future.

Taking the time to build a shared future is critical since it enables everyone to move past deciding where we are going and then to focus on how we are going to get there together. The next step is to make sure you fully understand the organization – the system – that will take us to that future.

Exercise 5.2 | **Think of your business as a system**

This exercise is meant to help you reinforce your understanding of the components of your organization and how they work together. It should help take some of the knowledge you're using implicitly and pull it out of your head so you and others can explicitly understand it to be able to make it better.

1. **Sketch out your diamond.** Use the diamond model below or draw one in the *Leading the Organization* section of your workbook. Add in appropriate details to the corners. Once your system is defined, you can use this model to troubleshoot problems. The solution to a challenge in any area will usually come from adjusting the two connecting corners.

2. **Draft your own system diagram.** Use the shape below or draw your own in the *Leading the Organization* section to sketch a system diagram for your organization. Think of this as a "bad draft" to get your internal critic to take a coffee break!

   a. Stay simple and sketch out the big pieces. Start on the left side with the input — your prospective clients. Draw your primary process in a few steps from left to right. If there are lots of variations, feel free to flowchart them out at a high level. Don't get stuck in the weeds!

   b. Put your primary assets and direction on the top, and your primary support and resources on the bottom.

   c. Describe the output of your process on the right side.

   d. Keep handy and tweak as needed so you know where to focus and adjust your organizational system.

3. **Get input and support from others.** Using either diagram, ask people who know your organization (employees, managers, key suppliers, even clients) to contribute. Find out what's missing or what you've assumed away.

Many leaders get stuck working in the tactical day-to-day and are unable to see the "big picture." Now that you have a simplified understanding of your organizational system as a whole, you can improve the system step-by-step by starting at the outcome and working on the steps and methods required to achieve it.

Exercise 5.3 | **Improve your ability to work backward.**

The following exercises are simple, short ways to examine and improve your ability to design goals and plans that start from the outcome and step back toward today. Using this approach, you can ensure the path to your desired goals is as effective as possible.

1. **Do a quick review of your company goals.** Grab your most current goal sheet and critically examine each goal. How much pull is there versus how much push? How intentional are the outcomes versus just an extension of what we do today? How holistic are your measurements of success versus how much are they focused on a single aspect of what you believe your company is all about? Document your conclusions in the *Leading the Organization* section of this workbook.

2. **Take a challenge and figure out the desired outcomes.** Pick something difficult and ask a few others, "What do you think the end goal is? If we all got to do the right thing, what's the final result?" Compare answers and look for overlaps to uncover shared understanding (or lack thereof). Document what you find in the *Leading the Organization* section.

3. **Build a bridge to shared outcomes.** Building on the step above, take that same problem – along with the shared understanding – to people and ask, "What comes right before we get there? What do we need to make that happen?" Keep asking until you can trace back to the next steps that you and others need to take to move directly toward the desired destination.

4. **Review and adjust reward systems.** It's tragically common how often functional goals and rewards are set up – mostly unintentionally – in ways that pit people and sections against each other rather than encourage people to work together. Do a quick review of your systems and ask, "How much do we have conflicting or zero-sum rewards?" Note your findings in the *Leading the Organization* section. Then identify one area where you could have collective rewards even if there are goals that conflict with each other. Reward optimization of the whole instead of optimization of individual or functional goals.

With clear, comprehensive, and shared outcomes to focus on, the next step is to smooth the path of the organization in that direction so the right things are the easiest things to do.

Exercise 5.4 | **Put friction where you want it**

Like a pair of ice skates that allow you to glide smoothly across an ice rink, the ideal situation reduces resistance in the direction you want to travel and increases resistance in the direction you don't want to go (sideways!). This exercise explores how to harness both aspects of friction to benefit your organization.

1. **Find out where others are being driven crazy.** Take a few minutes and ask your key people what's holding them back: "What drives you crazy about your job? What do you wish you could change? What have you resigned yourself to doing in your work?" Capture your findings in the *Leading the Organization* section, then partner up with people to change the system and reduce friction so it's easier for them to do the right thing.

2. **Figure out where the organization is getting bad results from the path of least resistance.** Take a few minutes and think about specific situations where the organization is getting unwanted results because the easiest thing isn't the right thing. It's usually easy to spot waste, and a bit harder to see missed opportunities. Make a list of possibilities in your *Leading the Organization* section, and prioritize them by the impact they have or could have on the organization. Brainstorm with people working in the affected area about how to add friction to help prevent mistakes.

3. **Use the force field, Luke.** Below or on a clean page of your **Leading the Organization** section, create a force-field diagram, titled with the challenge you want to tackle. Draw a vertical line in the center. On the left side, draw and label arrows representing all the mechanisms that support moving in the direction you want to go – physical, emotional, and mental. The bigger the force, the longer the arrow. On the right side, draw and label all the forces that are resisting forward progress.

Commuting by bike more often

Have a nice bike | Takes longer

Want to exercise | Needs tuneup

Wife likes to bike | Bad weather

Then start taking action to remove or reduce the items on the right and increase or add items on the left. In my example of commuting by bike, buying a good rain jacket and tuning up the bike may be all I need to do to allow the forces on the left to gain the upper hand.

This tool is great for analyzing what could be holding you back – and remember that those aren't always negative things but could be positive benefits of not taking action. A valuable resource on the web is **Mind Tools** - http://www.mindtools.com/pages/article/newTED_06.htm - which has this tool among many. When you invest time up front to provide structure that makes the right action the default action, everyone wins every time that action takes place. Being deliberate about shaping your organization's design to use the path of least resistance everywhere possible can dramatically increase the energy and effort moving the organization forward.

Exercise 6.1 | **Reinforce the integrity of your system**

Running your organization so that the design is strengthened the more you use it is vital to having an organization everyone can rely on. These exercises will help you raise your awareness of where you may be slowly degrading the capacity of your organization because of the way you run the system.

1. **Examine your exception tolerance level.** How messy are you allowing your system to be? There can be a fine line between building on individual strengths and having exceptions be the rule. You may want to check with some of your trusted staff or colleagues if your tolerance level (or lack thereof) is negatively affecting the organization. Capture your findings in the *Leading the Organization* section.

2. **Check your track record.** Use the table below to help you reflect on the performance of the organization. Title the left column "Results" and the right column "Reasons."
   a. List where you and your team are getting the results you expect and need.
   b. Add to the list where you and the team are *not* getting good results.
   c. Write your best guess for the reason(s) behind each success and failure in the right column.
   d. Finally, look for patterns that relate to how much the issue or the reasons were exceptions. Note them and start looking for opportunities to eliminate the exceptions in your system.

Results	Reasons

3. **Shift your system**. With the results of the previous exercise, take a few minutes and note the changes needed to increase system integrity going forward by incorporating any exceptions into the system. Pick a change that has the most significant impact for the least amount of effort, and work with your team to implement the change. Hint: the change needed is likely to be something your people have wanted to do for some time. You may have a hard time staying out of their way once you provide your team the authority to do something about it.

Part of achieving efficiency with your systems is to ensure you are looking at the outcomes first and adjusting as needed to get the result you really need. The next key is ensuring that everyone involved has information on the outcomes they are achieving so they can self-adjust to get better results.

Exercise 6.2 | **Get everyone cruising**

These exercises are just the tip of the iceberg. It's one thing to improve people's awareness of standards and how they are performing to them. It's another to modify the system to provide people ongoing information and understanding to enable them to adjust as needed to hit the standard.

1. **Check your people's feedback equipment.** Enter into a dialogue with your key people around "What is success, and what do we need to know or have to achieve it?" Your goal is to increase your awareness as well as theirs of what we're aiming for, what information we get, and what that information is telling us or not telling us. Note their answers and your thoughts in the *Leading the Organization* section. Look for simple ways to create individual "Your Speed Is" information.

What is success?	How do we know we are successful?	How we could add feedback to know

2. **Connect people to what's most important.** Pull out your company's vision, strategy, goals, and objectives. In your *Leading the Organization* section, make a quick list of the information you get that lets you know both you and the company are on track. Ask yourself how much of this everyone knows and understands. If you come up with some blanks, start a five-minute sharing session at each staff meeting to help people learn what matters.

Key goal or objective	How do I know we are on track?

3. **Start opening your window shades.** Determine what you could share that would help other people better understand the results and how they could make a difference personally. Choose one or two pieces of information and start sharing. Be sure to help people understand the "why behind the what" by asking questions that explore the impact beyond the numbers. Document your findings in whichever section you believe is most appropriate!

Once you've established effective feedback loops, you will be enabling people to correct their own behaviors to hit the goals. The next practice is about ensuring that the systems and resources, along with policies and procedures, are managed to enable the best in people instead of trying to simply reduce errors.

Exercise 6.3 | **Nurture skilled system mechanics**

The best people to help shape structure are those who are intimately involved with the results that structure produces. Understanding their experience is a very powerful way to make an organization simultaneously fit the people and what needs to get done.

1. **Find out how your organization is doing.** Put yourself in a prospect's, client's, or coworker's shoes. Ask yourself on a scale from zero to ten how well your organization is getting consistent results and at the same time encouraging the best from each person. Validate with a trusted team member or, better yet, a trusted customer or client. Be sure to keep your defenses down and openly explore the feedback you receive. If you've created pages for these individuals, jot down your answers there. Otherwise, use the ***Leading the Organization*** section to capture responses.

2. **Shift the way you engage with people around systemic issues.** Think about your top three organizational challenges. How could you engage people differently in solving them such that their best qualities would be called forth? Spend a few minutes each with three people finding out how they see the challenges. Your findings should be less about things to avoid and more about changes that will enable the right things to happen in the first place. Again, document on individual pages or in the ***Leading the Organization*** section.

3. **Have a sacred-cow barbeque.** Spend a few minutes thinking about which rule or process requirement simply no longer serves the organization or the people. Spend about twice as long validating your thoughts with a trusted agent. Be sure to capture your thinking. Change the rule – and be prepared to be mostly thanked and have at least one person complain that he liked it the old way.

If you've tackled even one exercise for each practice, you've started some big ripples in your organization, in your people, and in yourself. Yet the last practice ensures that we continue to pick up the right kind of pebbles to make the right kind of impacts that steadily move our organization and people forward. Maintaining everything at status quo is as possible as holding a ripple still.

Exercise 6.4 | **Use your laurels as a springboard for the future**

The excellence you've helped make happen in your organization will set a new standard, not just in the results you've gotten, but also in the confidence of the team in creating their own future. Your continued role is therefore to keep providing gentle, consistent pressure toward increased levels of excellence. As Oliver Cromwell once said, "He who stops being better stops being good."

1. **Celebrate a recent success.** Publicly recognize a person or team who has made an improvement that impacted results. This will also have the Ripple Effect of encouraging others to make improvements. [Note: If you have a difficult time finding something to celebrate, either you are already doing everything perfectly, or your organization may be too difficult to change. In the latter case, try knocking down barriers. See *Make the right things easy*, practice 5.4.]

2. **Evaluate how you track success.** Review how important goals, objectives, and metrics are tracked and provided to the organization, and the frequency of measurements. How do we know when things are going well or are going poorly? How certain are we of a real trend and that we're tracking the right information? Are the measurements timely enough to make adjustments and improve results? If needed, take action to improve the quality system of measurements, feedback, and adjustment. Resist the urge for perfect solutions; just make things better.

3. **Figure out where your benchmarks are.** Write a list of organizations in your industry that you would like to emulate. Add other organizations that operate under similar conditions. For example, Southwest Airlines benchmarked NASCAR pit crews to figure out how to fuel and turn their planes faster! Think about the results you'd like to achieve and you can find great examples in unusual places. Another benefit if you cross industries is that you're more likely to get cooperation and breakthrough ideas.

4. **Conduct Lessons Learned reviews.** Developed by the US Army, simple reviews at the end of each exercise or project can help organizations remind themselves what went well, what went poorly, how we would do it differently next time, and who needs to know. Taking a few minutes at the end of a meeting to find out what the group would like to Start doing, Stop doing, and Continue doing can make an amazing difference to the next and subsequent meetings.

By ensuring the organization pays attention to results and has the confidence to make changes to itself, you will be on the path to becoming what Peter Senge defines as a learning organization – that is, an organization that can flex and change as needed to make the impact it exists to make on the world.

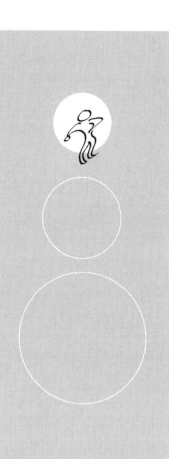

Personal Insights — Leading Yourself

Use the following pages to capture the results of exercises and thoughts as you focus on improving your self leadership.

Principle 1 –
Leaders' effectiveness is proportional to how well they know themselves.

Decide what matters most
Your personal values are the best compass for your unique journey.

Chart your own course
Picturing your own personal future helps you see what steps to take – or not – to get there.

Know where you're awesome
People often don't recognize their own strengths – and you cannot tap what you do not know.

Principle 2 –
Leaders are judged more by what they don't than by what they do.

Do the hard stuff
Doing what's most important is the hardest and most rewarding work you will do as a leader.

Risk and be resilient
Leaders deal with the unknown first – and then must adjust to achieve the outcome.

Charge your own batteries
Caring for and strengthening yourself ensures effectiveness that makes your leadership possible.

Personal Insights—
Leading Others

Use the following pages to capture the results of exercises and thoughts as you focus on improving your leadership of others.

Principle 3 –
People discover their best selves through being respected by a leader.

Trust or have nothing
Like oil in an engine, trust makes everything run well. Without it you get friction and struggle.

Mission first. People second. You? Last
You need to be able to put others' need before yours.

Assume most of your stories are wrong
Prejudging another's intentions limits both of you more than you realize.

Look for diamonds in the dirt
Helping others see their own strengths allows their greatness to shine.

Help them figure out how to fish
Create ownership by asking questions that help others struggle and grow.

Principle 4 –
Leaders are judged more by what they don't than by what they do.

Meet them at eye level
Starting from where people are enables everyone involved to see what's needed next.

Lead from a half-step ahead
Staying close yet just ahead of those you lead reduces the pressure on everyone.

Light their torches
To help others see their own paths, spark the fuel of their personal passions.

Be their outfitter and guide
Equip others for their own journeys and tackle constraints they cannot.

Coworker / Employee

Name

Role

Coworker / Employee

Name

Role

Coworker / Employee

Name

Role

Coworker / Employee

Name

Role

Coworker / Employee

Name

Role

Client / Customer

Name

Role

Client / Customer

Name _____   Role _____

Client / Customer

Name

Role

Client / Customer

Name   Role

Client / Customer

Name

Role

Personal Insights— Leading the Organization

Principle 5 –
Organizations are designed to get the results they are getting.

Use everyone's crayon in the picture
When people see their influence in a shared vision of the future, they become owners.

Know what's in the black box
An understanding of your organization's parts and connections is required to help everything work together.

Work backward from the outcome
Start with where you want to end up, then trace back each preceding step to today.

Make the right things easy
Create systems that get the best result by default and make the worst result hard to achieve.

Principle 6 –
Organizations creating waste are generating opportunities for improvement.

Do or do not...there is no exception
Take exception to exceptions. Either change the system or just don't do it.

Put a speedometer on everyone's dashboard
Feedback loops are one of the most powerful methods for self-driven performance improvement.

Enable eggshell structure
Focus on helping people do their best instead of preventing the worst.

Go beyond status quo
Organizations naturally decline, so for optimum results, actively experiment and continuously tweak.

About the author

To Chris, living is about high tech tools and low tech lifestyles. Teams and individuals. Courage and consideration. Exercise and chocolate.

After years of building Legos® and treehouses around the world, Chris went to school for a Mechanical Engineering degree and a Masters in Business Administration. His experiences in the military and the corporate world taught him that great leadership can be learned, and that everyone is a leader.

Chris wants to help create a world where people care for and respect themselves, each other, and the environment. To do so he believes we must inspire businesses to be a greater positive force in the world. His calling is to model, teach, and support businesses and people to be that positive force.

Keep making ripples

Visit rippleleader.com for a downloadable copy
of this workbook and other useful tools.

For more information and support on how to put these principles
and practices into action, please contact a Trebuchet Group
consultant at trebuchetgroup.com.

Made in the USA
Columbia, SC
13 January 2020